THE TOP TEN MOST BEAUTIFUL PIECES TO PLAY ON PIANO

WISE PUBLICATIONS
part of The Music Sales Group
London/New York/Paris/Sydney/Copenhagen/Berlin/Madrid/Hong Kong/Tokyo

Published by
Wise Publications
14-15 Berners Street,
London W1T 3LJ, UK.

Exclusive Distributors:
Music Sales Limited
Distribution Centre, Newmarket Road,
Bury St Edmunds, Suffolk IP33 3YB, UK.
Music Sales Corporation
180 Madison Avenue, 24th Floor,
New York NY 10016, USA.
Music Sales Pty Limited
Level 4, Lisgar House,
30-32 Carrington Street,
Sydney, NSW 2000 Australia.

Order No. AM1012253
ISBN 978-1-78558-400-8

Compiled by Naomi Cook.
Notes written by Sandy Burnett.

Photographs courtesy of:
Page 5: Jack Mitchell/Getty Images
Page 10: Fine Art Images/Heritage Images/Getty Images
Page 17: Mansell/The LIFE Picture Collection/Getty Images
Page 20: Ullstein bild/ullstein bild via Getty Images
Page 24: Leemage/UIG via Getty Images
Page 29: Hulton Archive/Getty Images
Page 35: Herbert Lambert/Mansell/The LIFE Picture Collection/Getty Images
Page 38: Hulton Archive/Getty Images
Page 52: Yulia Mahr

Printed in the EU.

THE TOP TEN MOST BEAUTIFUL PIECES TO PLAY ON PIANO

Music is a magical thing. Its ability to stir up powerful emotions through a harmonic gesture or melodic inflection is a mysterious and wonderful phenomenon. In this volume we've collected the most moving pieces to play on piano, covering a wide range of moods and eras.

Some were written with other forces in mind, for example, the hauntingly spiritual 'Miserere' by Allegri, written for the Sistine Chapel in Rome, Handel's tender 'Lascia Ch'io Pianga', which enchanted London opera audiences three centuries ago, and the collection's closing work by Max Richter, a beautiful piece originally written for strings. Elsewhere we have piano music through and through; a gentle nocturne by Chopin, and two separate 'moonlight' works by Beethoven and Debussy. Regardless of their original form, these creations possess a quality that can be hard to define in words, so all that's left to do is turn the page and play…

ADAGIO FOR STRINGS

COMPOSER: Samuel Barber
COMPOSED: 1938

A sombre start to our collection, this *Adagio For Strings* by Samuel Barber is exquisitely written and not too hard to play. The melody line moves mostly in quavers and the fabric of the music is simple, but it's amazing how much Barber manages to say with very limited resources. The piece has had a fascinating journey: originally the second movement of a string quartet, Barber transcribed it for string orchestra and it was taken up by the great Arturo Toscanini, who premiered the piece with the NBC Symphony Orchestra. American audiences listening to the premiere live on the radio felt that

Barber's *Adagio* spoke directly to them, and what they had suffered during the dark era of the Great Depression.

In the succeeding years the piece has regularly been brought into service at times of great national suffering: it was played to commemorate the deaths of major public figures such as Presidents Franklin D Roosevelt and John F Kennedy, as well as Princess Diana, and to commemorate the victims of the 9/11 attacks. It's also been used in films, most notably as the theme tune to the Oliver Stone movie, *Platoon.*

ADAGIO FOR STRINGS

Samuel Barber

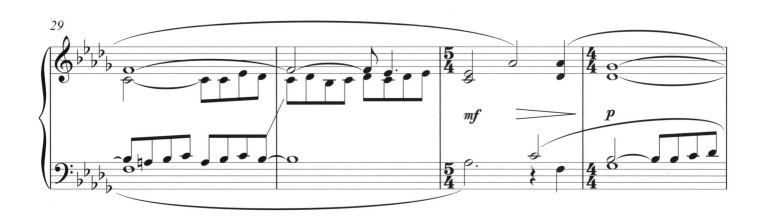

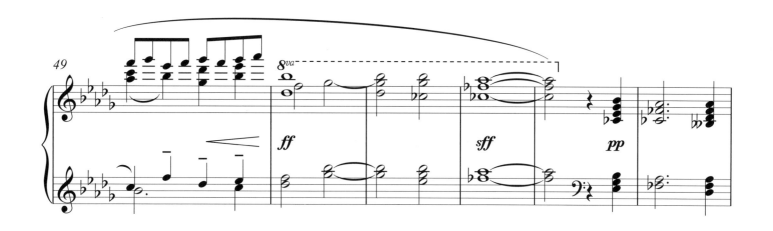

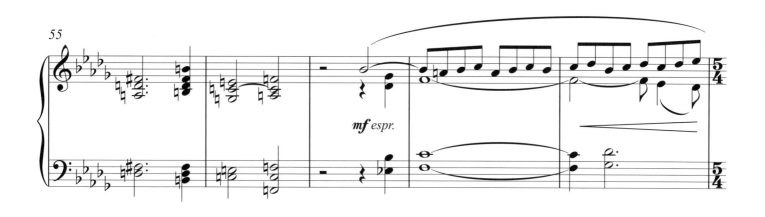

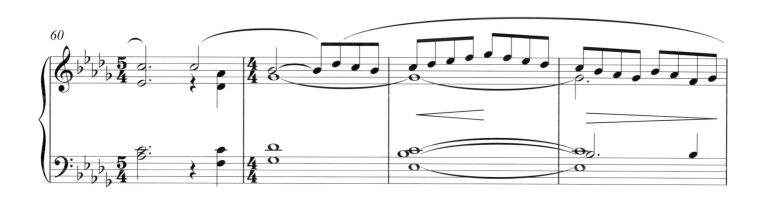

CLAIR DE LUNE
NO. 3 FROM *SUITE BERGAMASQUE*

COMPOSER: Claude Debussy
COMPOSED: *c.* 1890–1905

Where would French music be without the great Claude Debussy? He helped to define a new sound for his era – a so-called 'impressionist' style of writing music. Completely different from what German composers were trying to achieve at the time, Debussy was creating sounds and ideas which were suggestive of something; if what he was suggesting isn't always exactly clear, that's part of the beauty of Debussy's musvic. Some of his inspiration came from the exotic music of the east, for example, the Javanese sounds that he heard played on the gamelan ensemble of percussion instruments. Another important inspiration came from the French poets of the day. In fact, this famous piece 'Clair De Lune' or 'Moonlight' takes its title from a poem of the same name by Paul Verlaine, which talks about 'souls … like landscapes, charming masks and bergamasks, playing the lute and dancing, almost sad in their fantastic disguises.' Debussy's piece, veiled in *una corda* and predominantly within a *pianissimo* dynamic, beautifully evokes the delicacy of those lines; it's, shall we say, the second most famous piece about moonlight in the entire piano repertoire?

CLAIR DE LUNE

NO. 3 FROM *SUITE BERGAMASQUE*

Claude Debussy

Calmato

Tempo I

pp morendo jusqu'à la fin

ANDANTE GRAZIOSO
THEME FROM *PIANO SONATA NO. 11 IN A MAJOR*, K331

COMPOSER: Wolfgang Amadeus Mozart
COMPOSED: 1783/4

In the early 1780s the brilliant Wolfgang Amadeus Mozart was riding high as a piano star in the world's music capital, Vienna; he'd just moved there to seek fame and fortune as a freelance virtuoso. It was at this time, when he was astonishing audiences with his stunning piano concertos, that he also wrote this intimate piece to be played at home. Unlike his concertos, this is a piece which is well within the abilities of an eleventary pianist: you don't need to be a Mozart-grade virtuoso to play this one!

This *Andante* comes from his eleventh piano sonata – the one that ends with the famous *Rondo Alla Turca*. While that closing movement is full of fire and energy, this piece is quite the reverse – the rocking feel of the movement makes it sound like a lullaby. Both right and left hands share the same rhythm for the first three bars, pointing up the gentle swing of the music; the thumb of the left hand brings out a repeated D, rather like the discreet drone of a bagpipe; and although Mozart marks *sf* or *sforzandi* now and again, they should be good-natured nudges rather than anything too violent.

ANDANTE GRAZIOSO

THEME FROM *PIANO SONATA NO. 11 IN A MAJOR, K331*

Wolfgang Amadeus Mozart

LASCIA CH'IO PIANGA
FROM *RINALDO*, HWV 7

COMPOSER: George Frideric Handel
COMPOSED: 1711

As one of Handel's best-loved opera arias, *Lascia Ch'io Pianga* was too good not to feature in this collection, so we've included this arrangement for solo piano. A word of warning about the speed: the melody in minims combined with the tempo indication of *largo* might encourage you to play the piece much too slowly; imagine the beat as crotchets at a walking pace, and that would be about right. There aren't usually too many markings or performance indications in Baroque era music like this, and that's the case here, so feel free to gently shape the music in a way that's right for you.

The aria itself comes from *Rinaldo*, the first Italian opera that Handel ever wrote for the London stage. Staging exotic operas with outlandish plots sung in a language that hardly anyone could understand was something that should never have worked – but, luckily for Handel, it did. The stunning staging had something to do with that, as did of course the beauty of the singing. What's more, Handel composed all of the music for this one in an incredible two weeks!

In the second act of *Rinaldo*, the heroine Almirena has been wrenched from her lover's arms by an evil sorceress, and she finds herself imprisoned in the gardens of an enchanted palace. There, she bemoans her fate in this beautiful aria.

LASCIA CH'IO PIANGA

FROM *RINALDO*, HWV 7

George Frideric Handel

MISERERE

COMPOSER: Gregorio Allegri
COMPOSED: 1638

In its original form scored for unaccompanied choir, Allegri's 'Miserere' is one of the most performed works of *a cappella* vocal music that there's ever been written, which is surprising when you think that the Vatican authorities wanted to keep the music a closely-guarded secret, and slapped a strict ban on any copy of it ever leaving the Sistine Chapel. This form of security was eventually breached, of course, and one of the guilty parties was the brilliant Wolfgang Amadeus Mozart. In 1770, passing through Rome as a teenager, he heard it performed just once and afterwards wrote out the whole thing from memory. Or so the story goes…

The sombre text, *Have mercy on me, O God*, comes from Psalm 51. One of the most expressive psalms of all, it's traditionally sung during Holy Week in Catholic acts of worship. When playing this transcription on the piano, you might like to try and emulate the spacious acoustic of the Sistine Chapel in your playing (if such a thing is possible). It's also worth bringing out the contrast between the chordal sections in which all voices of the choir sing the syllables of the text at the same time, and the flowing sections in which individual lines interlace with each other, with the famous high Cs at bars 22 and 49 emerging to brilliant effect.

MISERERE

Gregorio Allegri

Slowly and solemnly ♩ = 100

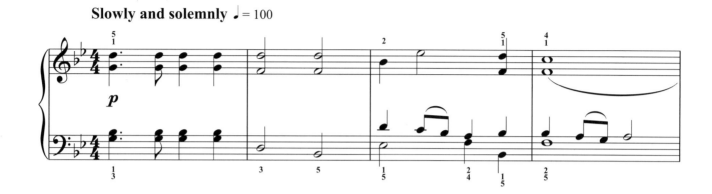

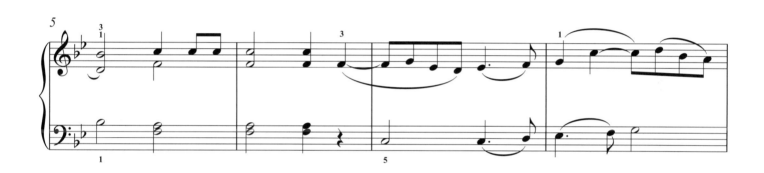

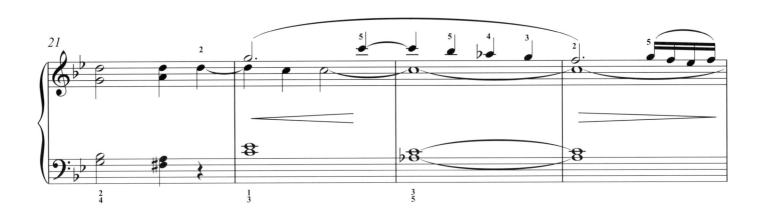

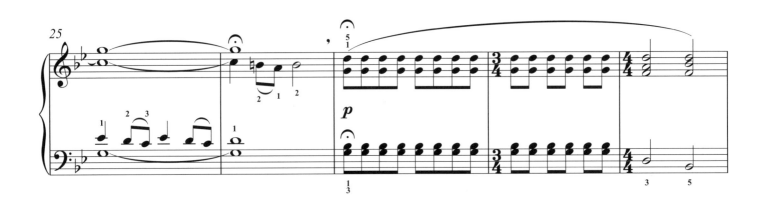

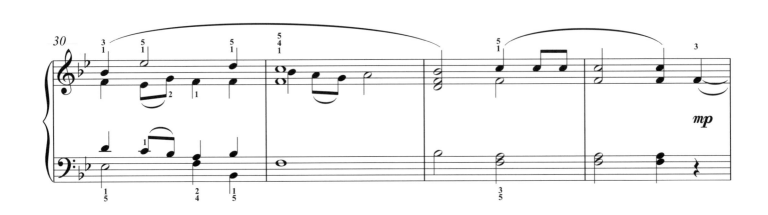

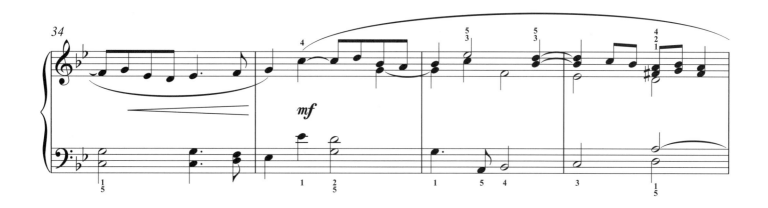

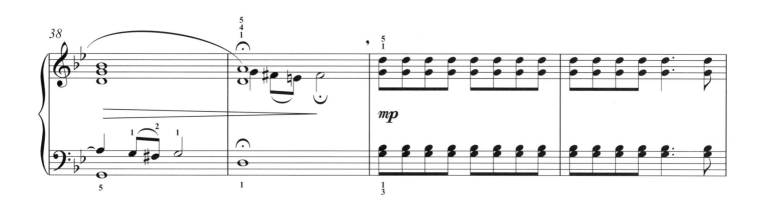

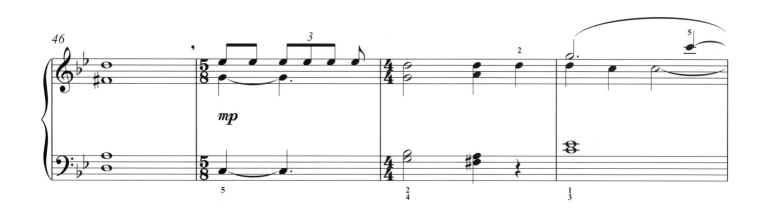

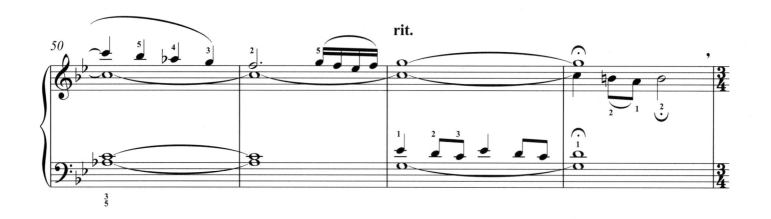

rit.

a tempo

pp sempre

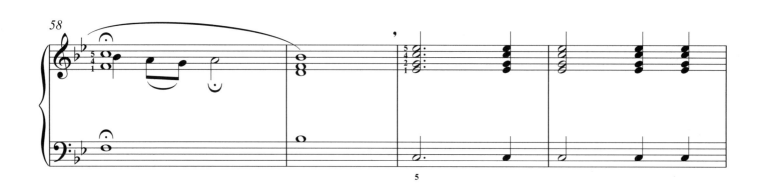

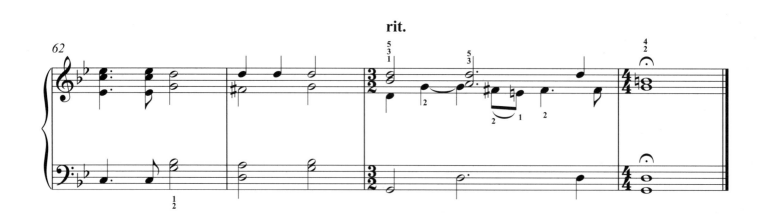

rit.

MOONLIGHT SONATA, OP. 27, NO. 2

COMPOSER: Ludwig Van Beethoven
COMPOSED: 1801

Ludwig Van Beethoven was famously unlucky in love; he had several fleeting passions with women over the years, none of which ever came to anything. One was with Countess Giulietta Guicciardi, one of his piano pupils. She had a portrait done of herself which she gave to Beethoven, and he kept it for the rest of his life. Beethoven dedicated his piano sonata Op. 27 No. 2 in C Sharp Minor to her, a work he described as 'quasi una fantasia.' Some thirty years later the poet Ludwig Rellstab came up with a catchier description. He wrote that the first movement – the one printed here – made him think of the moonlight shining on the water of Lake Lucerne. The name 'Moonlight Sonata' has stuck ever since, possibly helping its popularity in the popular consciousness as one of the best-loved piano pieces ever.

The famous right hand triplets should flow with minimum disruption – note the word *sostenuto* (sustained) in the tempo marking, and use the soft pedal as indicated to keep a veil over the music. The term *slentando*, which appears in the last line, is one that doesn't come round very often – Beethoven is asking the performer to slow down just a little here to bring the music to a gentle close.

MOONLIGHT SONATA, OP. 27, NO. 2

Ludwig Van Beethoven

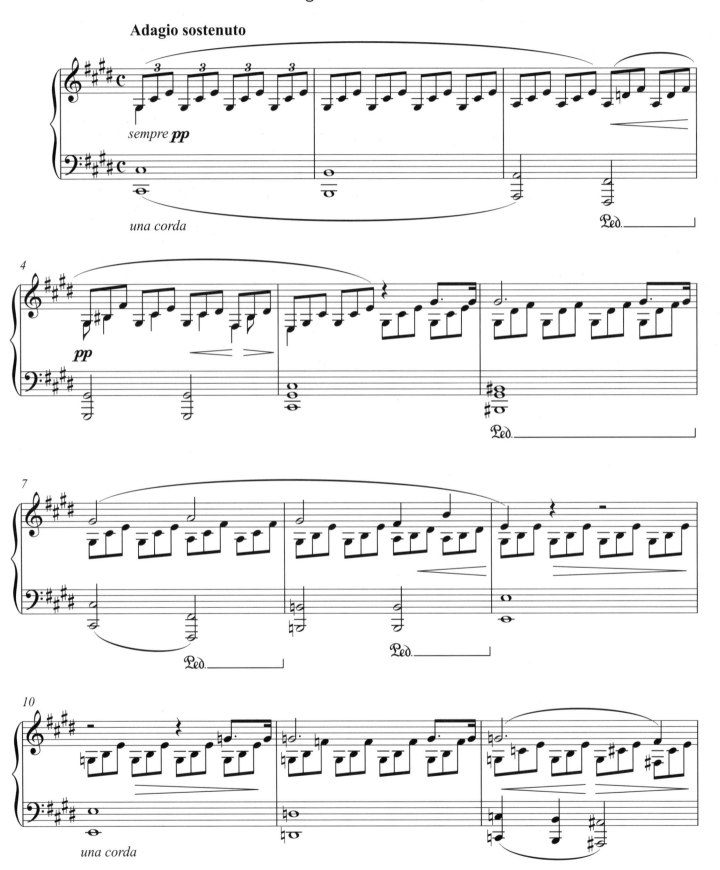

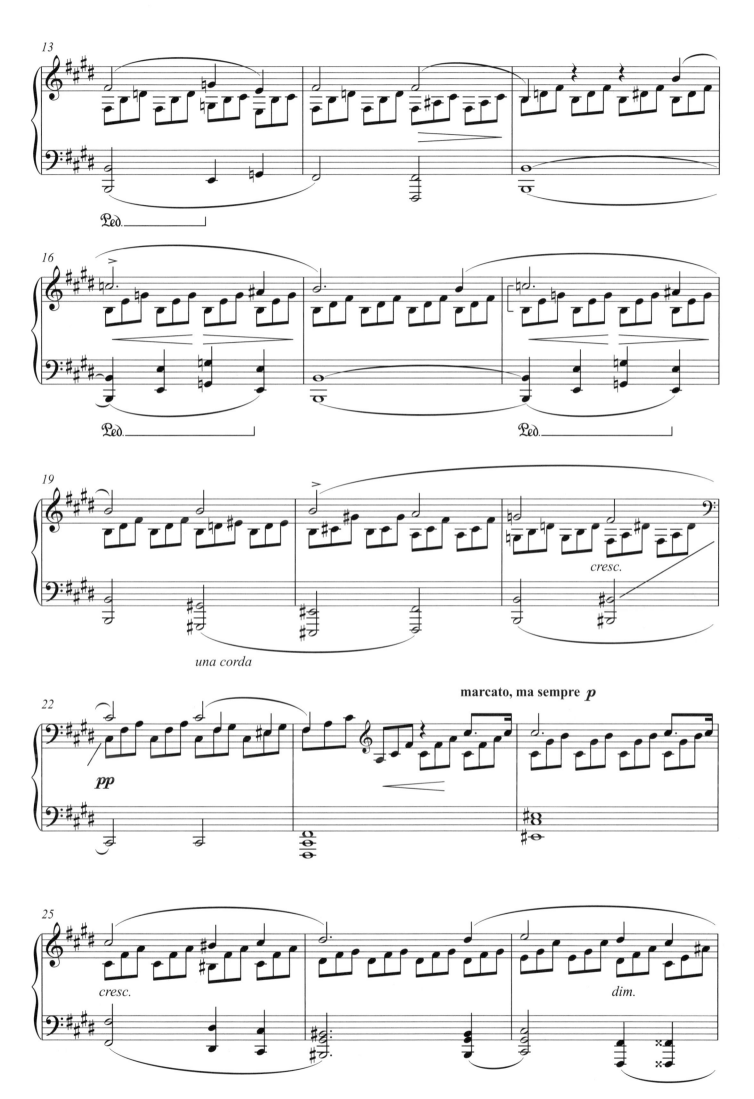

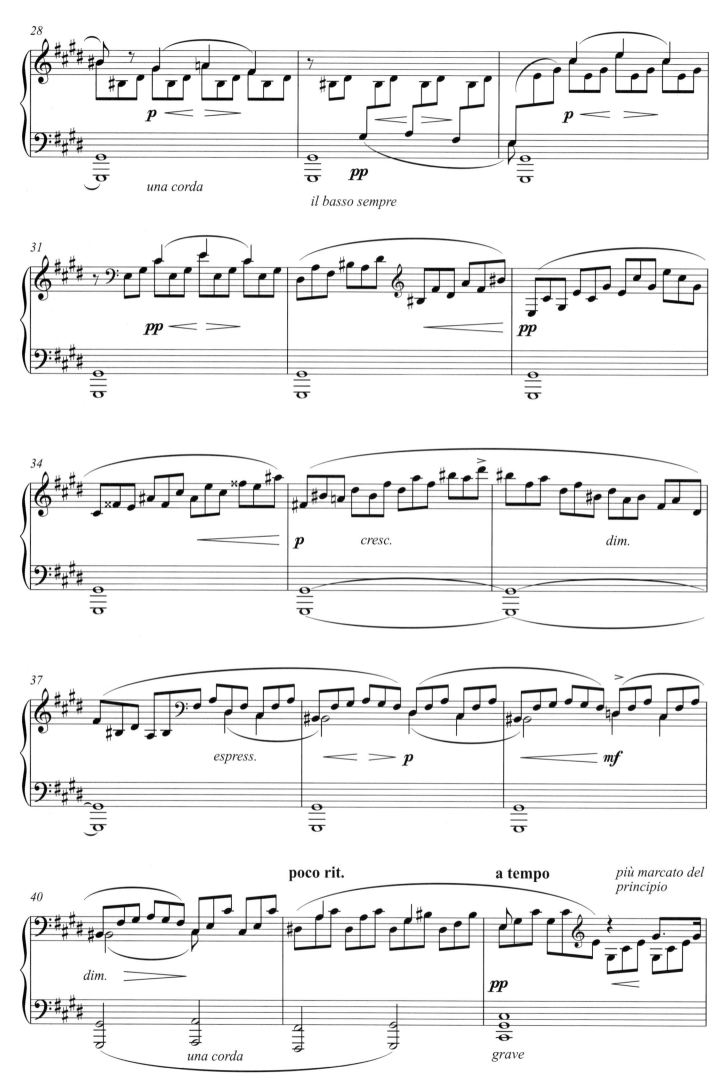

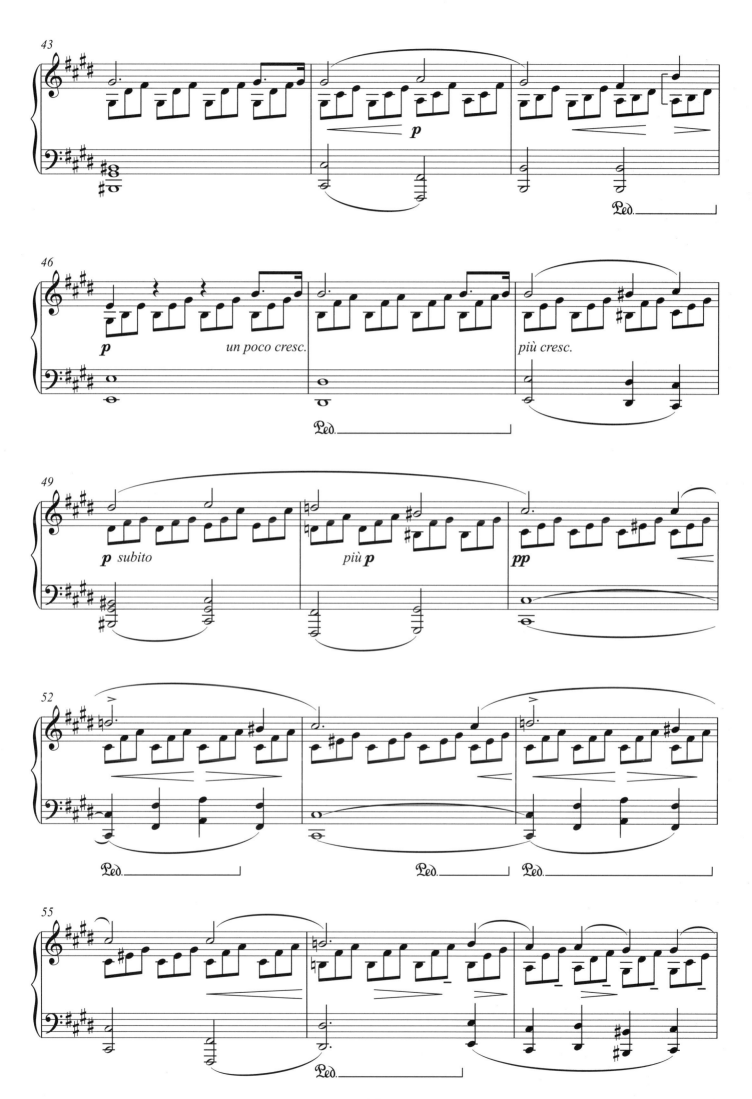

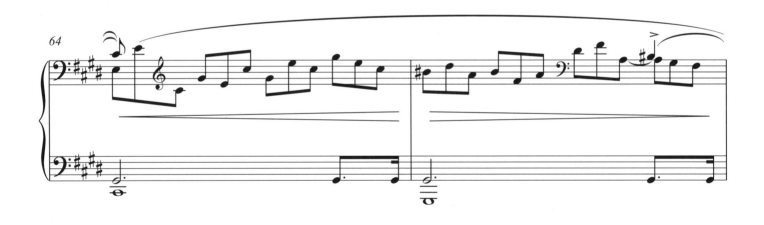

34

NIMROD
FROM *ENIGMA VARIATIONS*, OP. 36

COMPOSER: Sir Edward Elgar
COMPOSED: 1899

This unforgettable and quintessentially English tune comes from the work that really established the reputation of Elgar in the British classical music scene: *Enigma Variations*. When they were performed for the first time, one of the reasons the new work caused so much interest was the intriguing dedication in the score: 'to my friends pictured within.' Each of the fourteen variations represents someone the composer knew; Elgar, who was a great lover of conundrums and puzzles, had headed each variation with oblique hints as to whom these people might be. 'Nimrod' – which is variation number nine – is the best-known of all; Elgar later revealed that it represented one aspect of the character and temperament of August Jaeger. He was a German-born musician who worked as the publisher of Elgar's music for the Novello firm. More than just a colleague, though, Jaeger did more than anyone apart from Elgar's wife to help the composer through some pretty tough times of depression and self-doubt. This piece, which also plays on Jaeger's name, – 'Nimrod' is the 'mighty hunter' mentioned in the Old Testament book of Genesis, and 'Jaeger' means huntsman in German – is a worthy tribute to Elgar's close friend.

NIMROD

FROM *ENIGMA VARIATIONS*, OP. 36

Sir Edward Elgar

NOCTURNE IN E♭ MAJOR, OP. 9, NO. 2

NO. 3 FROM *SUITE BERGAMASQUE*

COMPOSER: Frédéric Chopin
COMPOSED: 1832

This is music of exquisite beauty and delicacy, the living image of Frédéric Chopin himself, a Polish pianist who took the salons of Paris by storm in the early 1830s. Elegance was his trademark, as well as the magical way he seemed to be able to sing with his fingers while playing the piano, the whole thing supported by the subtle use of the pedal, which was always impeccably judged. Refinement was all; Chopin couldn't bear people playing the piano forcefully – or 'like a dog barking,' as he used to say. Since Pleyel pianos were his brand of choice during that time, Chopin chose to dedicate this beautiful Nocturne to Camille Pleyel, the director of the family firm.

Espressivo dolce is Chopin's opening performance indication here, so nothing too emphatic is required. While this is pianistic music through and through, there's another influence in this Nocturne: that of the opera house. If you like, you can think of your right hand as an opera diva and your left as a sympathetic orchestra and conductor, there merely to accompany the melody.

NOCTURNE IN E♭ MAJOR, OP. 9, NO. 2

NO. 3 FROM *SUITE BERGAMASQUE*

Frédéric Chopin

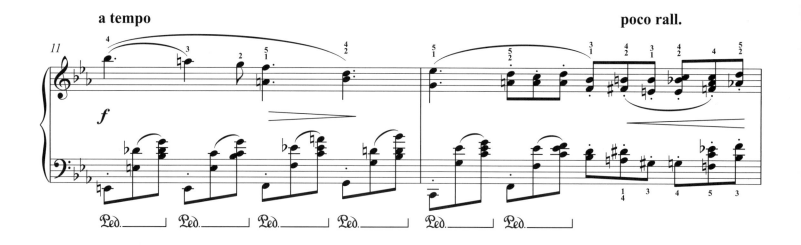

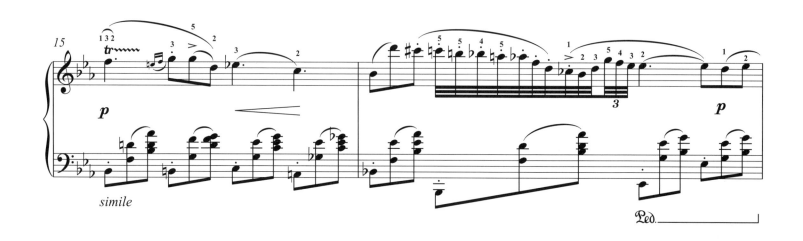

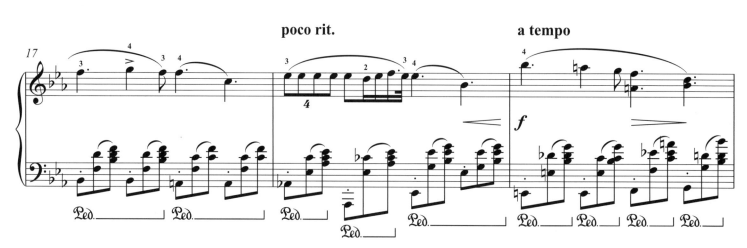

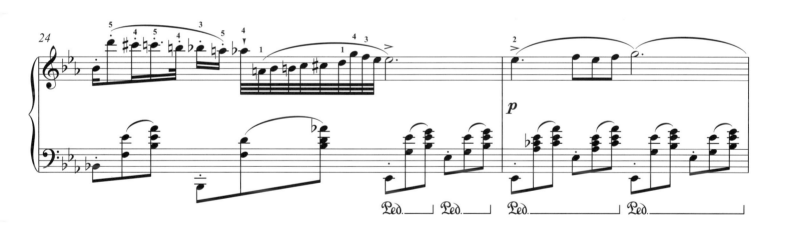

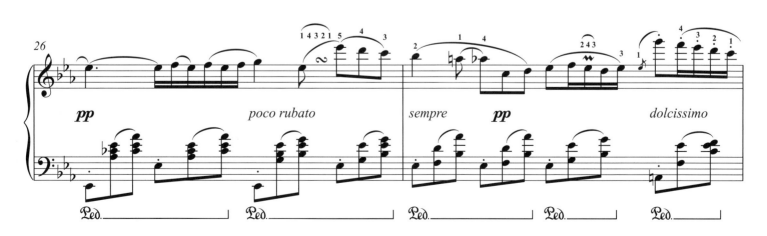

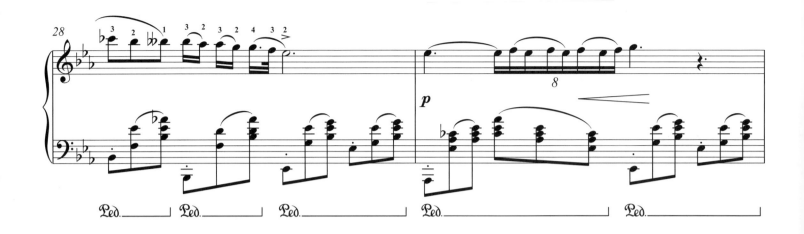

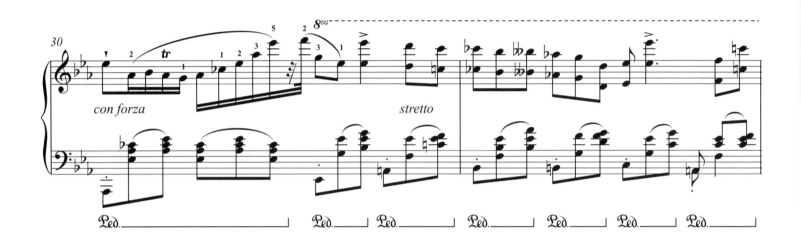

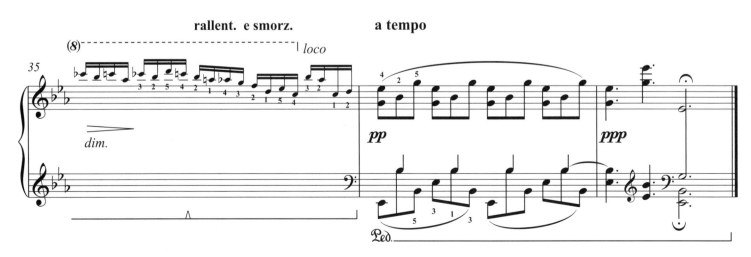

NUVOLE BIANCHE

COMPOSER: Ludovico Einaudi
COMPOSED: 2004

The music of Ludovico Einaudi has in recent decades become nothing less than a worldwide sensation. Born in Turin in 1955, some early experience of writing his own music on guitar led him to study at the Verdi Conservatory in Milan; after studying orchestration with Luciano Berio he won a scholarship to the Tanglewood School in the United States. He has collaborated with other art forms in the mediums of film, television and dance, and has worked alongside kora musicians from Mali and a duduk player from Armenia, as well as the conventional orchestral forces of the Royal Liverpool Philharmonic. Above all though, what has touched the hearts of his audiences is the purity of his compositions for solo piano, which

he himself often performs live in concert to sell-out audiences across the globe. Managing to be both simple to play and hear, and rich in emotional scope, his music has become a phenomenal success.

'Nuvole Bianche' is a piece which combines static calm with a gentle sense of forward movement. Use the metronome marks as a guide to ease the music gently forward, bearing in mind that it should take its time to develop. With the *poco a poco accelerando* marking at the foot of the third page, be aware that the increase in tempo and the growth in dynamic can take their time to unfold. There's no need to get too loud, or too fast, too early!

NUVOLE BIANCHE

Ludovico Einaudi

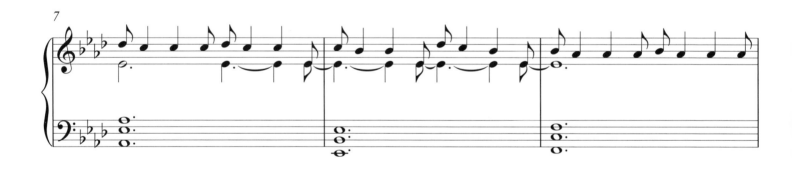

ON THE NATURE OF DAYLIGHT/WRITTEN ON THE SKY

FROM *SHUTTER ISLAND*

COMPOSER: Max Richter
COMPOSED: 2004

Bringing the composition styles of the classical tradition together with new forms of music-making such as punk rock and ambient music has in recent years been the central approach of the German-born British composer Max Richter. He studied at the Royal Academy of Music in London and also with Luciano Berio – as did the previous composer, Ludovico Einaudi. Like Einaudi, it's the power of his musical message delivered through simple musical means, and his frequent solo performances and recordings that represent some of the most important aspects of his music; the way he's brought the different musical elements together has seen him hailed as one of the most significant composers of the last decade.

No stranger to collaborating with other art forms, Max Richter has seen his work being used in over fifty films. One of them is the 2010 feature film *Shutter Island* directed by Martin Scorsese and starring Leonardo DiCaprio and Emily Mortimer; this haunting tune plays over the closing credits. Originally scored for strings, it's based on a series of four-bar chordal patterns, gently sustained, over which the quavers of melody soar and hover. In this piano version, we've given the left hand accompaniment a gentle pianistic figuration, but the overall effect should be nothing more than a sustaining support for the beautiful melody above it.

ON THE NATURE OF DAYLIGHT/ WRITTEN ON THE SKY

FROM *SHUTTER ISLAND*

Max Richter

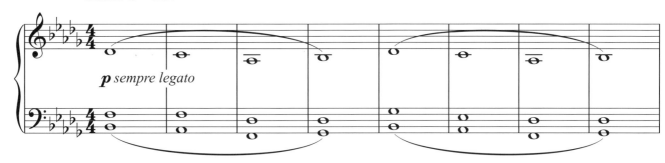

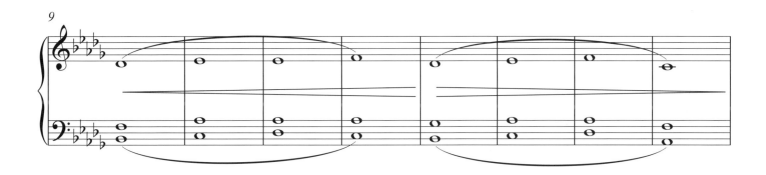

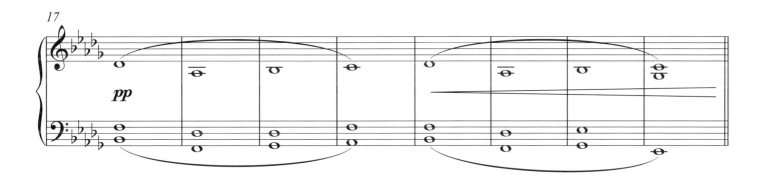

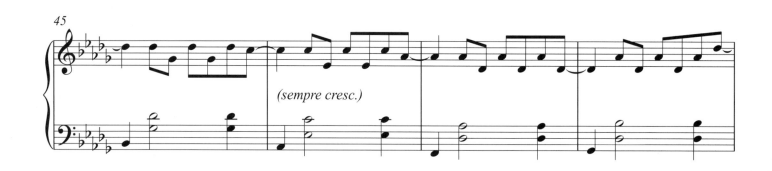

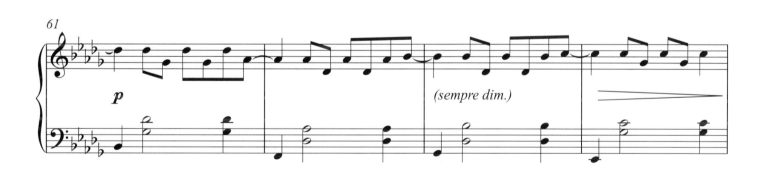

ALSO AVAILABLE...

THE TOP TEN CLASSICAL PIANO PIECES EVERY BEGINNER SHOULD LEARN	THE TOP TEN MOST BEAUTIFUL PIECES TO PLAY ON PIANO	THE TOP TEN CHRISTMAS SONGS TO PLAY ON PIANO	THE TOP TEN LOVE SONGS TO PLAY ON PIANO	THE TOP TEN PIANO SONGS OF ALL TIME
AM1012231	AM1012253	AM1012484	AM1012275	AM1012242

THE TOP TEN CLASSICAL PIANO PIECES EVERY BEGINNER SHOULD LEARN (AM1012231)

BERCEUSE
from *Dolly Suite*, Op. 56
FAURÉ

THE DOLL'S COMPLAINT
FRANCVK

FÜR ELISE
BEETHOVEN

FUGUE
from *Five Miniature Preludes And Fugues*
ROWLEY

PAVANE DE LA BELLE AU BOIS DORMANT
from *Ma Mère L'Oye*
RAVEL

MELODIE
from *Album Für Die Jugend*
SCHUMANN

MINUET IN F MAJOR, K2
MOZART

PRELUDE NO. 1 IN C MAJOR, BWV 846
BACH

SARABANDE
from *Keyboard Suite In D minor*, HWV 437
HANDEL

SARABANDE
EINAUDI

THE TOP TEN MOST BEAUTIFUL PIECES TO PLAY ON PIANO (AM1012253)

ADAGIO FOR STRINGS
BARBER

ANDANTE GRAZIOSO
Theme from *Piano Sonata No. 11 In A Major*, K331
MOZART

CLAIR DE LUNE
No. 3 from
Suite Bergamasque
DEBUSSY

LASCIA CH'IO PIANGA
from *Rinaldo*, HWV 7
HANDEL

MISERERE
ALLEGRI

MOONLIGHT SONATA, OP. 27, NO. 2
BEETHOVEN

NIMROD
from *Enigma Variations*, Op. 36
ELGAR

NOCTURNE IN E♭ MAJOR, OP. 9, NO. 2
CHOPIN

NUVOLE BIANCHE
EINAUDI

ON THE NATURE OF DAYLIGHT/ WRITTEN ON THE SKY
from *Shutter Island*
RICHTER

THE TOP TEN CHRISTMAS SONGS TO PLAY ON PIANO (AM1012484)

ALL I WANT FOR CHRISTMAS IS YOU
MARIAH CAREY

FAIRYTALE OF NEW YORK
THE POGUES
FEAT. KIRSTY MacCOLL

HAVE YOURSELF A MERRY LITTLE CHRISTMAS
FRANK SINATRA

JINGLE BELL ROCK
BOBBY HELMS

MERRY XMAS EVERYBODY
SLADE

SANTA BABY
EARTHA KITT

SANTA CLAUS IS COMIN' TO TOWN
EDDIE CANTOR

WALKING IN THE AIR
Theme from *The Snowman*
PETER AUTY/ALED JONES

WHITE CHRISTMAS
BING CROSBY

WINTER WONDERLAND
DEAN MARTIN

THE TOP TEN LOVE SONGS TO PLAY ON PIANO (AM1012275)

AT LAST
ETTA JAMES

CLOSE TO YOU (THEY LONG TO BE)
THE CARPENTERS

(EVERYTHING I DO) I DO IT FOR YOU
BRYAN ADAMS

THE FIRST TIME EVER I SAW YOUR FACE
ROBERTA FLACK

HOW DEEP IS YOUR LOVE
BEE GEES

I WILL ALWAYS LOVE YOU
WHITNEY HOUSTON

MAKE YOU FEEL MY LOVE
ADELE

MY HEART WILL GO ON
from *Titanic*
CÉLINE DION

MY IMMORTAL
EVANESCENCE

YOUR SONG
ELTON JOHN

THE TOP TEN PIANO SONGS OF ALL TIME (AM1012242)

BRIDGE OVER TROUBLED WATER
SIMON & GARFUNKEL

CLOCKS
COLDPLAY

DON'T STOP BELIEVIN'
JOURNEY

LIFE ON MARS?
DAVID BOWIE

ORDINARY PEOPLE
JOHN LEGEND

SKINNY LOVE
BIRDY

SOMEONE LIKE YOU
ADELE

SOMEWHERE ONLY WE KNOW
KEANE

A THOUSAND MILES
VANESSA CARLTON

TINY DANCER
ELTON JOHN

THE TOP TEN CONTEMPORARY CLASSICAL PIECES TO PLAY ON PIANO	THE TOP TEN MOST CALMING SONGS TO PLAY ON PIANO	THE TOP TEN FILM THEMES TO PLAY ON PIANO	THE TOP TEN POP SONGS EVERY BEGINNER PIANIST SHOULD LEARN	THE TOP TEN JAZZ SONGS TO PLAY ON PIANO
AM1012286	AM1012319	AM1012264	AM1012297	AM1012308